Seven a

A. L. Griffiths

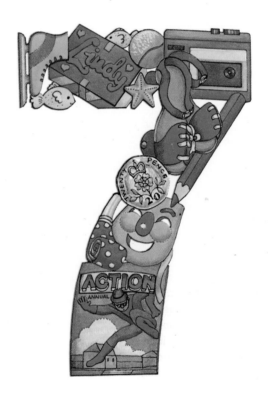

OLIVER & BOYD

Oliver & Boyd
Pearson Education Limited
Edinburgh Gate,
Harlow,
Essex, CM20 2JE

An Imprint of Addison Wesley Longman Ltd

First published 1986
Thirteenth impression 1999

Set in 12pt Linotype Melior Roman
Designed and illustrated by Scorpion Pica
Printed in China
GCC/13

ISBN 0 05 003924 5

The Publisher's policy is to use paper manufactured from
sustainable forests.

LENGTH

MASS (WEIGHT)

CAPACITY

TIME

CHECKING UP

MIXED REVISION

1 Favourite months of pupils in Emma's class

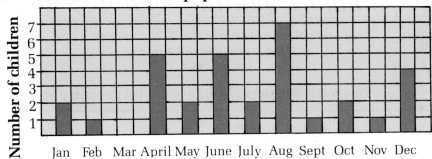

1 Which is the favourite month?
2 How many more pupils prefer December to February?
3 How many pupils altogether like June or July or August?
4 How many pupils like one of the first three months?
5 How many pupils like a month in the second half of the year?
6 How many pupils are in Emma's class?
7 Two girls voted for the month of June.
   How many boys voted for that month?

2 Boys and girls in Class 1

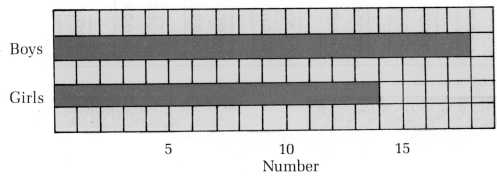

1 How many boys are there in Class 1?
2 How many girls are there in Class 1?
3 How many more boys than girls are there?
4 How many children are there altogether?
5 Fourteen boys stay to school lunch. How many boys go home to lunch?
6 Class 2 has nine more girls than Class 1. How many girls are there in Class 2?
7 A third of the boys and half of the girls have pets. How many children have pets?

3

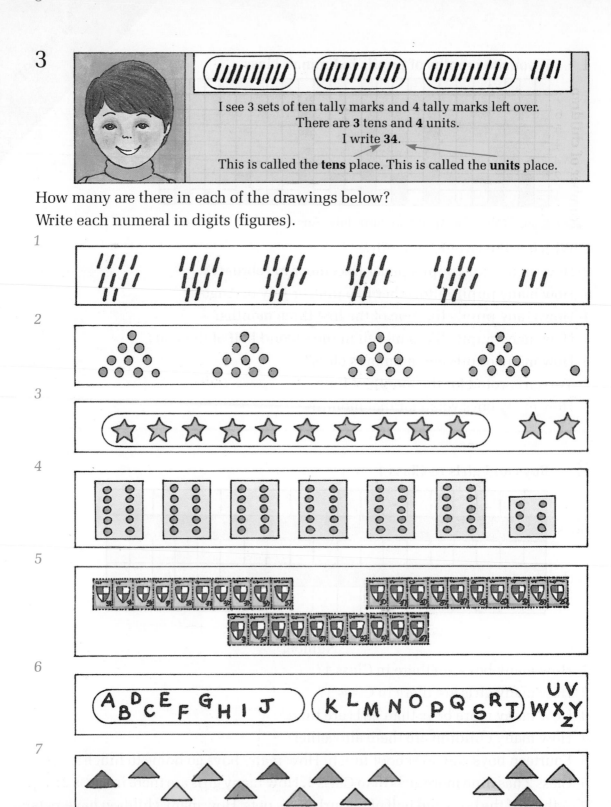

I see 3 sets of ten tally marks and 4 tally marks left over.
There are **3** tens and **4** units.
I write **34**.

This is called the **tens** place. This is called the **units** place.

How many are there in each of the drawings below?

Write each numeral in digits (figures).

1

2

3

4

5

6

7

4

Show each of the numbers below by drawing tally marks like these.

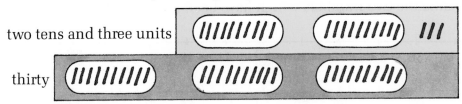

two tens and three units

thirty

1 three tens and three units   2 two tens and nine units
3 four tens and no units   4 twenty
5 twenty-eight   6 twenty-six
7 seventeen

5

The number shown on the abacus is twenty-three (23).
Draw a simple abacus to show each of these numbers.

1 fourteen   2 sixty
3 fifty-four   4 seventy-seven
5 11   6 80
7 36

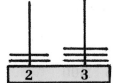

6

Write these abacus numbers in digits.

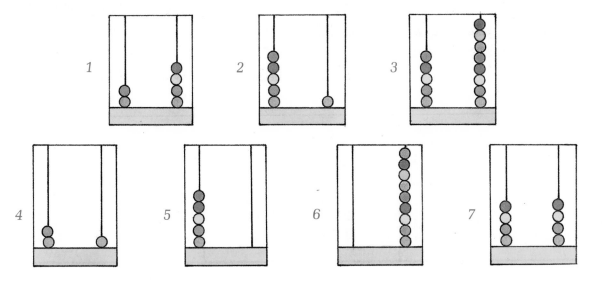

7

Here are parts of number lines.
Name the two numbers which have been missed out of each line.

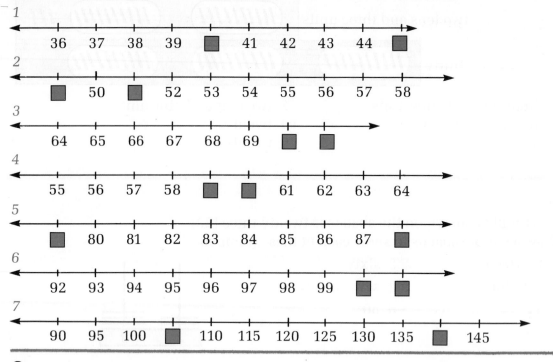

1   36 37 38 39 ■ 41 42 43 44 ■

2   ■ 50 ■ 52 53 54 55 56 57 58

3   64 65 66 67 68 69 ■ ■

4   55 56 57 58 ■ ■ 61 62 63 64

5   ■ 80 81 82 83 84 85 86 87 ■

6   92 93 94 95 96 97 98 99 ■ ■

7   90 95 100 ■ 110 115 120 125 130 135 ■ 145

8

Use the pictures below to answer the questions at the top of page 9.

| A | B | C |
| D | E | F |

1 How many triangles are there in picture A?
2 How many circles are there in picture C?
3 How many triangles are there in picture D?
4 How many squares are there in picture E?
5 How many triangles are there altogether in A and D?
6 How many squares are there altogether in B and E?
7 How many circles are there altogether in C and F?

9

Use the pictures in Exercise 8 to answer these questions.
1 How many more squares are there in B than E?
2 How many more triangles are there in A than D?
3 How many more circles are there in C than F?
4 Find the difference between 83 and 60.
5 What is the total of 30 and 67?
6 Add 23 and 70.
7 How many more must be added to 37 to make 50?

10

Use the pictures above to answer these questions.
1 How many trees are there altogether in picture A and picture E?
2 How many are there altogether in B and F?
3 How many stars are there altogether in C and G?
4 How many are there altogether in D and H?
5 How many more trees are there in E than in A?
6 How many more stars are there in C than in G?
7 How many more are there in D than in H?

11

1 Add 56 and 32.
2 Add eighteen to sixty-one.
3 Find the total of fifty-five and thirty-four.
4 What is the sum of 14, 21 and 32?
5 What is the difference between 56 and 32?
6 Subtract 35 from 87.
7 Take 42 from 89.

12 These pictures will help you to answer the questions below.

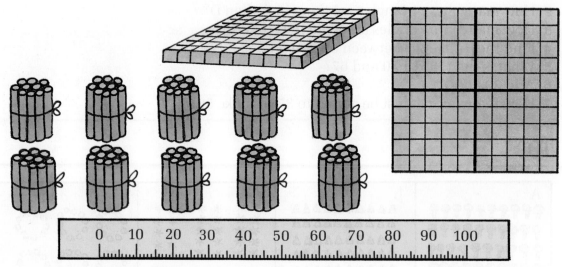

1 How many must be added to each of these numbers to make a hundred?
   a 70   b 20   c 50
2 Here are some cricket scores.
   How many less than a century (100) is each score?
   a 93   b 65   c 74
3 Write in digits a half of a hundred.
4 Write in digits a quarter of eighty.
5 Write in digits a quarter of a hundred.
6 Write in digits a tenth of a hundred.
7 Write in digits a tenth of fifty.

13

Here are the scores of some cricketers.
What is each cricketer's total score?

1 35 and 15   2 23 and 16
3 80 and 15   4 28 and 42
5 24 and 66   6 61 and 19
7 38 and 40

14

1 Take 35 from 80.
2 How many more is 40 than 17?
3 What must you add to 71 to make 85?
4 What is the sum of 25 and 65?
5 Add 64 and 24.
6 What is the total of 40, 23 and 17?
7 What number is twenty-eight more than twenty-two?

15

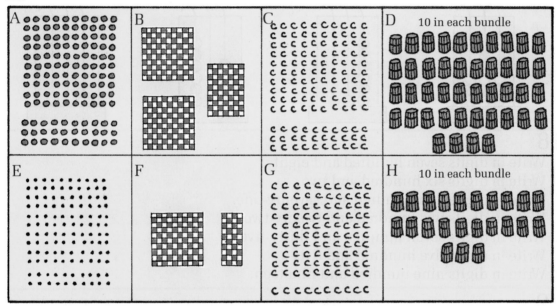

Use the pictures above to answer these questions.
1 How many large dots are there in picture A?
2 How many small squares are there in picture B?
3 How many letters are there in picture C?
4 How many rods are there in picture D?
5 How many small dots are there in picture E?
6 How many small squares are there in picture F?
7 How many rods are there in picture H?

16

Use the pictures in Exercise 15 to answer these questions.
1 How many dots are there altogether in A and E?
2 How many small squares are there altogether in B and F?
3 How many letters are there altogether in C and G?
4 How many rods are there altogether in D and H?
5 How many more dots are there in A than in E?
6 How many more small squares are there in B than in F?
7 How many more letters are there in C than in G?

17 Write each of these abacus numbers in digits.

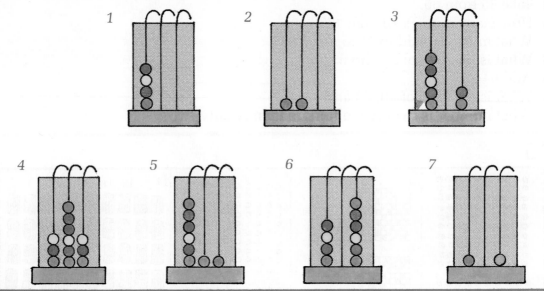

18
1 Write in digits seven hundred and eighty.
2 Write in digits six hundred and two.
3 Write in digits four hundred and seventy-one.
4 Write in digits two hundred and twenty-two.
5 Write in digits seven hundred and thirty-five.
6 Write in digits five hundred and five.
7 Write in digits nine hundred and nineteen.

19
Write each of these abacus numbers in digits.

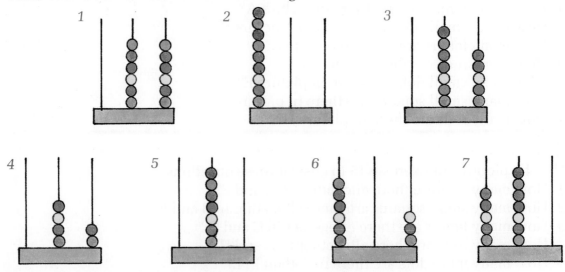

20

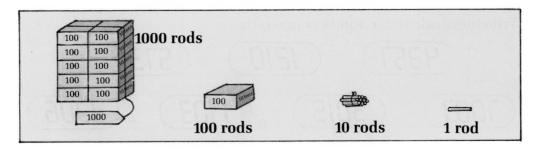

Write in digits the number of rods in each of the pictures below.

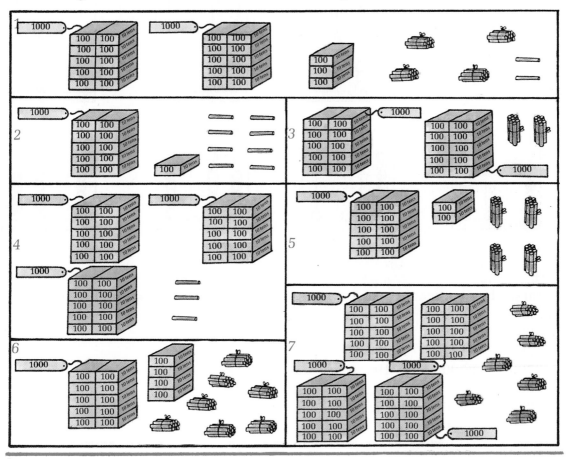

21

1 Write in digits four thousand, five hundred and forty-six.
2 Write in digits three thousand and thirty-three.
3 Write in digits five thousand and thirteen.
4 Write in digits eight thousand, one hundred and one.
5 Write in digits one thousand and eleven.
6 Write in digits nine thousand and nine.
7 Write in digits seven thousand, seven hundred.

22

Write these calculator numbers in words.

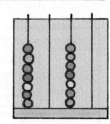

1 **4357**   2 **1210**   3 **5730**

4 **7007**   5 **5015**   6 **1703**   7 **3306**

23

Write these abacus numbers in digits.

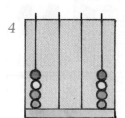
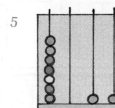
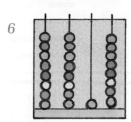
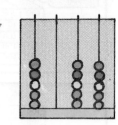

24

Arrange the numbers in each line in order of size from the least to the greatest.

1 798	300	2592
2 3867	7683	6738
3 2309	2137	2098
4 6709	6790	6719
5 3033	3003	3030
6 7080	7800	7008
7 3299	3300	3298

25

Write down the numeral which goes in place of each ■.

1   $752 = 700 + ■ + 2$

2   $4398 = 4000 + ■ + 90 + 8$

3   $3472 = 3000 + 400 + ■ + 2$

4   $7864 = 7000 + ■ + 60 + 4$

5   $3219 = ■ + 200 + 10 + 9$

6   $4943 = 4000 + 900 + 40 + ■$

7   $6589 = 6000 + ■ + 80 + 9$

26

Write down the numeral which goes in place of each ▭.
1 6000 + 7 + 50 + 400 = ▭
2 90 + 3000 + 5 + 200 = ▭
3 7 + 100 + 80 + 7000 = ▭
4 30 + 400 + 40 + 6 + 1000 = ▭
5 300 + 20 + 500 + 3000 = ▭
6 4 + 200 + 60 + 700 + 20 + 2000 = ▭
7 4 + 5 + 400 + 300 + 6000 = ▭

27

1 In 4768 which digit means ones?
2 In 6321 which digit means thousands?
3 In 3075 which digit means tens?
4 In 4783 which digit means hundreds?
5 Write down the numeral that means 3 thousands and 3 tens.
6 Write down the numeral that means 5 thousands, 0 hundreds, 3 tens and 1 one.
7 What numeral can be put in place of **n** in this addition sentence?
        9863 = 9000 + **n** + 60 + 3

28

7305 = 7000 + 300 + 5

Now write these in the same way.

1 3867 = ■ + ▲ + ▼ + ▭   2 4783 = ■ + ▲ + ▼ + ▭
3 3067 = ■ + ▲ + ▼   4 9760 = ■ + ▲ + ▼
5 3705 = ■ + ▲ + ▼   6 7060 = ■ + ▲
7 5009 = ■ + ▲

29

1 What is the greatest number that can be named using each of the digits
   3, 4, 8 and 2 once only?
2 What is the smallest number that can be named by using the digits 3, 4, 8 and 2?
3 Name the number that is 11 more than 7807.
4 Name the number that is 101 more than 4763.
5 Name the number that is one thousand and one more than
   six thousand, seven hundred and twenty-five.
6 What is under each ▪?
7 What comes between?

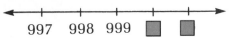

30

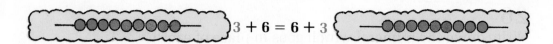

$3 + 6 = 6 + 3$

> Remember a number sentence with an equals sign is called an **equation**.
> $3 + 2 = 5$ is an **equation**.

Solve these equations by finding the number that **n** stands for.

1 $4 + 3 = \mathbf{n} + 4$
2 $48 + \mathbf{n} = 17 + 48$
3 $9 + 6 = 6 + \mathbf{n}$
4 $300 + 9 = \mathbf{n} + 300$
5 $\mathbf{n} + 8 = 8 + 5$
6 $418 + 219 = 219 + \mathbf{n}$
7 $17 + \mathbf{n} = 8 + 17$

31

> We sometimes use brackets to tell us which part must be worked first.
> In this addition:
> $4 + (2 + 1)$
> we find the sum of 2 and 1, then the sum of 3 and 4.

What numeral can be written in place of ■ in each of these equations?

1 $(6 + 4) + 3 = ■ + 3$
2 $(6 + 2) \times 2 = ■$
3 $9 + (8 + 7) = 9 + ■$
4 $6 + (2 + 2) = ■$
5 $(8 + 9) + 6 = ■ + 6$
6 $3 \times (3 + 2) = ■$
7 $(6 \times 3) + 8 = ■ + 8$

32

1 $5 + 3 + 4 = ■$
2 $3 + 5 + 4 = ■$
3 $4 + 3 + 5 = ■$
4 $3 + 4 + 5 = ■$
5 $4 + 5 + 3 = ■$
6 $5 + 4 + 3 = ■$

7 Write out this sentence, putting in the correct answer from those in the brackets. Whenever we add 3 numbers, it ▓▓▓▓▓ matter which 2 numbers we add first.

(does, does not)

33

Look at this addition: $46 + 9 = \square$.

Think:

since $6 + 9 = 15$

then $40 + 6 + 9 = 55$

Now try these.

1 $78 + 8 = \square$

2 $146 + 5 = \square$

3 $87 + 7 = \square$

4 $9 + 67 = \square$

5 $46 + 9 = \square$

6 $8 + 49 = \square$

7 $85 + 7 = \square$

34

Look at this addition: $29 + 16 = \square$.

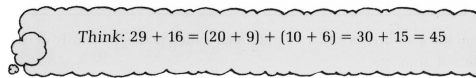

Think: $29 + 16 = (20 + 9) + (10 + 6) = 30 + 15 = 45$

Now try these.

1 $27 + 13 = \square$

2 $67 + 24 = \square$

3 $38 + 16 = \square$

4 $83 + 45 = \square$

5 $29 + 44 = \square$

6 $64 + 93 = \square$

7 $34 + 38 = \square$

35

1 $46 + 50 = \square$

2 $123 + 9 = \square$

3 $70 + 29 = \square$

4 $4 + 127 = \square$

5 $63 + 74 = \square$

6 $968 + 5 = \square$

7 $92 + 84 = \square$

36

We have learned that we can arrange numbers for addition in any order we like.
Remember this useful law when you are working out these additions.

1 $7 + 38 + 3 = \square$

2 $7 + 6 + 3 + 4 = \square$

3 $28 + 67 + 2 = \square$

4 $40 + 29 + 60 = \square$

5 $7 + 6 + 6 + 3 + 1 = \square$

6 $25 + 37 + 25 = \square$

7 $36 + 4 + 150 = \square$

37

1 Find the total of sixteen, seventeen and four.

2 What is the sum of 106 and 390?

3 Work out the number that is 73 more than 27.

4 Add all the even numbers between 3 and 9.

5 Add the total of 4, 9 and 1 to the sum of 9 and 7.

6 Write out this addition,
    putting in the missing digits.

$$\begin{array}{r} \star 8 \\ + 1\star \\ \hline 4\,2 \end{array}$$

7 Which of these signs, $<$, $>$ or $=$, can replace ⬤ in this number sentence?

$$400 + 300 + 0 \; \bigcirc \; 400 + 0 + 3$$

38

> Can you remember the addition and subtraction **families** ?
>
> This is the **family** for 4, 7 and 11:
>
> $4 + 7 = 11$ $7 + 4 = 11$ $11 - 4 = 7$ $11 - 7 = 4$

Write out the 2 additions and 2 subtractions which make the family of each of these sets of numbers.

1 3, 9 and 12   2 9, 15 and 6

3 5, 8 and 13   4 5, 9 and 14

5 16, 9 and 7   6 17, 8 and 9

7 8, 15 and 7

39

1 $763 - 100 = $ ◆   2 $873 - 43 = $ ▼

3 $574 - 103 = $ ▼   4 $746 - 220 = $ ◆

5 $436 - 34 = $ ◆   6 $865 - 123 = $ ▲

7 $768 - 260 = $ ▲

Use a calculator to check your answers.

40

1 Take nine from sixteen

2 Subtract eight from forty-seven.

3 What is the difference between fifty-four and six?

4 How many more than seven is twenty-five?

5 How many less than eighty is six?

6 What number is four less than a hundred and one?

7 Subtract eight from sixty-five.

41

1 $70 - 13 =$ ◼
2 $91 - 46 =$ ◼
3 $90 - 19 =$ ◼
4 $100 - 22 =$ ◼
5 $91 - 22 =$ ◼
6 $43 - 27 =$ ◼
7 $57 - 39 =$ ◼

42

1 Write five thousand and fifty in digits.

2 Write the abacus number in words.

3 Solve this equation. What number does **n** stand for?

$$(7 + 8) + 5 = \textbf{n} + 7$$

4 Take the sum of the even numbers between 1 and 5 from the sum of the odd numbers between 2 and 6.

5 Add the difference between 3 and 9 to the sum of 3 and 9.

6 $(0 + 3) + (3 - 0) =$ ◼

7 A length of ribbon 80 centimetres long is cut into two pieces. One piece is 37 centimetres long. How long is the other piece?

43

Write $>$, $<$ or $=$ in place of each ⬤.

1 $9 + 6$ ⬤ $6 + 7$
2 $63 + 13$ ⬤ $76 - 13$
3 $9 + 8$ ⬤ $20 - 1$
4 $9 + (4 - 1)$ ⬤ $(9 + 4) - 1$
5 $17 - 8$ ⬤ $10 + (6 + 3)$
6 $292 - 90$ ⬤ 100
7 $(14 + 5) - 3$ ⬤ $14 + 3$

44

Write out these in full, putting the correct digit in place of each ▲ and ◼.

1
```
   4▲
 − ◼7
 ────
   22
```

2
```
   4 4
 + ▲◼
 ────
   7 9
```

3
```
   ▲◼
 +5 8
 ────
   9 0
```

Copy, and write $+$ or $-$ in place of each ◼.

4 7 ◼ $4 = (13 - 3) + 1$
5 78 ◼ $12 = 6 + 60$
6 $70 + 6 = 79$ ◼ 3
7 $5 + (4 + 7) = 10$ ◼ 6

45

1 What was the total number of goals scored by Peter, David and Ali?

Top goal scorers

Mark	●	●	●	●	●	●	●	●	●	●	●	●	●	●
Abdul	●	●	●	●	●	●	●	●	●					
Peter	●	●	●	●	●	●	●							
Ali	●	●	●	●	●	●	●	●	●	●				
David	●	●	●	●							● stands for 1 goal			

2 What was the total number of goals scored by the two highest scorers?

3 How many more goals did Mark score than Peter and David together?

4 The whole team scored a total of 50 goals. How many goals were scored by the rest of the team?

5 How many more goals did Mark, David and Abdul score than Ali and Peter?

6 Mark scored a total of 33 goals this season and last.
How many did he score last season?

7 Twenty-eight of these goals were scored in home matches.
How many were scored in away matches?

46

1 What is the distance from the rugby ground to the church?

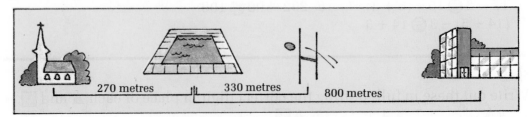

270 metres   330 metres   800 metres

2 Work out the distance from the school to the rugby ground.

3 What is the distance from the school to the church?

4 How much farther is it from the swimming pool to the rugby ground than from the swimming pool to the church?

5 What is the distance in kilometres from York to Dunbar?

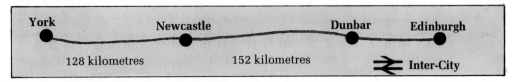

6 The distance from Newcastle to Edinburgh is 200 kilometres.
   What is the distance from Dunbar to Edinburgh?
7 How many more kilometres is the distance from Newcastle to Edinburgh than
   from Newcastle to York?

47

1 In the numeral 4708 what does the 7 mean —
   7 thousands, 7 hundreds, 7 tens or 7 units?
2 Write =, < or > in place of ⬤.

   $86 + 3$ ⬤ $3 + 8$ tens

3 What is the smallest four-digit number you can name using each of the
   digits 3, 7, 9, 1 once only?
4 What is the largest four-digit number you can name using each of the digits
   1, 2, 3, 4 once only?
5 What digit must be written in place of ★ in this addition?

$$\begin{array}{r} 3 \\ \star \\ +14 \\ \hline 22 \end{array}$$

6 In a gymnastics club there are 17 girls and 3 more boys than girls.
   How many children are in the club?
7 Ali has 63 marbles. He has 17 green marbles, 23 red marbles,
   and the rest are blue. How many blue marbles does he have?

48

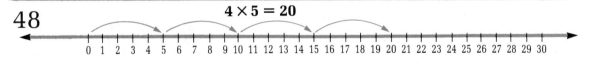

$$4 \times 5 = 20$$

Look closely at each of these number lines, then write a multiplication
equation, like the one shown above.

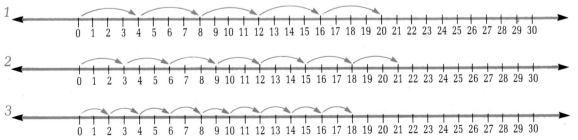

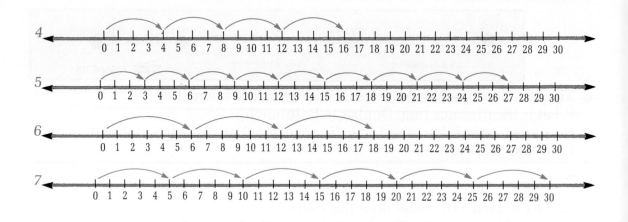

49

Write a multiplication equation like this to fit each of the pictures below.

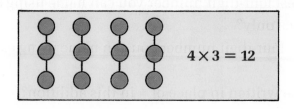

$4 \times 3 = 12$

1

2

3

4

5

6

7

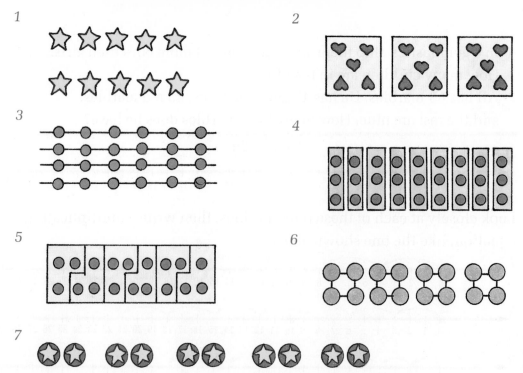

50

Look how the numbers grow. Write the next five numbers for each row.

1	2	4	6	8	10	?	?	?	?	?
2	3	6	9	12	15	?	?	?	?	?
3	4	8	12	16	20	?	?	?	?	?
4	5	10	15	20	25	?	?	?	?	?
5	6	12	18	24	30	?	?	?	?	?
6	10	20	30	40	50	?	?	?	?	?
7	9	12	15	18	21	?	?	?	?	?

51

$$4 + 4 + 4 + 4 + 4 = \blacksquare \quad 5 \times 4 = 20$$

Write a multiplication equation like the one above for each of these additions.

1 $3 + 3 + 3 + 3 + 3 + 3 + 3 = \blacksquare$

2 $5 + 5 + 5 + 5 + 5 + 5 + 5 + 5 = \blacksquare$

3 $6 + 6 + 6 + 6 + 6 = \blacksquare$

4 $2 + 2 + 2 + 2 + 2 + 2 + 2 + 2 = \blacksquare$

5 $10 + 10 + 10 + 10 + 10 + 10 + 10 = \blacksquare$

6 $5 + 5 + 5 + 5 + 5 + 5 = \blacksquare$

7 $4 + 4 + 4 + 4 + 4 + 4 + 4 + 4 = \blacksquare$

52

1 John, David and Peter shared some marbles equally and then found they each had 3 red and 6 green. How many marbles were there altogether?

2 Each of the 27 pupils in Class 1 has a box holding ten coloured pencils. How many coloured pencils do they have altogether?

3 Emma has 9 beads and Nisha has twice as many. How many beads do they have altogether?

4 Solve this equation: $(6 + 4) \times (7 + 3) = n$.

5 Three girls and five boys each sold six concert tickets.
How many tickets were sold in all?

6 Write this number sentence in full: $4 \times (4 \times 2) = \blacksquare$.

7 Solve this equation: $n + 698 = 750$.

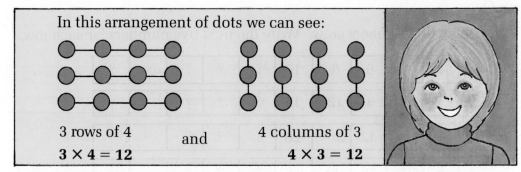

24

53

In this arrangement of dots we can see:

3 rows of 4   and   4 columns of 3

3 × 4 = 12   **4 × 3 = 12**

Write two multiplication facts for each of these drawings.

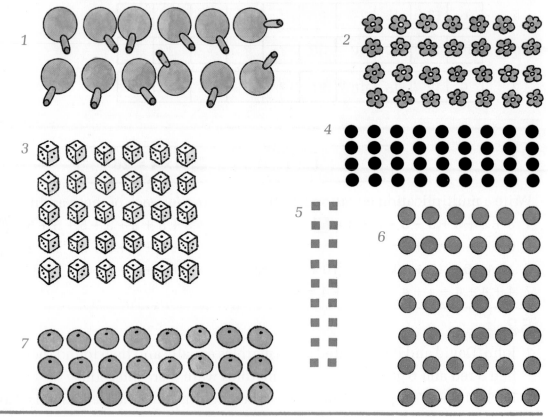

54

Write out these statements, putting the correct numeral in place of each ▢ and △.

1 21 = ▢ times △ or △ times ▢   2 27 = ▢ times △ or △ times ▢

3 45 = ▢ times △ or △ times ▢   4 42 = ▢ times △ or △ times ▢

5 15 = ▢ times △ or △ times ▢

6 35 = ▢ times △ or △ times ▢

7 14 = ▢ times △ or △ times ▢

55

We have already learned that in addition we can add numbers in any order.
Does the order in which we multiply numbers affect the product?
(Remember the answer when we multiply is called the **product**.)

Find these products.

1   $4 \times 2 \times 1 = \blacksquare$ $1 \times 2 \times 4 = \blacksquare$ $2 \times 4 \times 1 = \blacksquare$
2   $3 \times 4 \times 5 = \blacktriangle$ $3 \times 5 \times 4 = \blacktriangle$ $4 \times 5 \times 3 = \blacktriangle$
3   $9 \times 3 \times 2 = \blacksquare$ $3 \times 2 \times 9 = \blacksquare$ $9 \times 2 \times 3 = \blacksquare$
4   $7 \times 5 \times 2 = \blacktriangle$ $2 \times 5 \times 7 = \blacktriangle$ $7 \times 2 \times 5 = \blacktriangle$
5   $3 \times 6 \times 5 = \blacksquare$ $6 \times 3 \times 5 = \blacksquare$ $5 \times 6 \times 3 = \blacksquare$
6   $2 \times 3 \times 5 = \blacktriangle$ $5 \times 2 \times 3 = \blacktriangle$ $3 \times 5 \times 2 = \blacktriangle$
7   $5 \times 4 \times 6 = \blacksquare$ $4 \times 6 \times 5 = \blacksquare$ $6 \times 5 \times 4 = \blacksquare$

56   Here is another useful mathematical law at work.

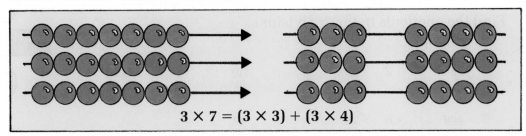

$$3 \times 7 = (3 \times 3) + (3 \times 4)$$

Remembering the law, find the number that $\blacksquare$ stands for in each of these.

1   $6 \times 5 = (6 \times 2) + (6 \times \blacksquare)$ 2 $4 \times 9 = (4 \times 4) + (4 \times \blacksquare)$
3   $5 \times 8 = (5 \times \blacksquare) + (5 \times 3)$ 4 $8 \times 7 = (8 \times 2) + (8 \times \blacksquare)$
5   $4 \times \blacksquare = (4 \times 3) + (4 \times 6)$ 6 $\blacksquare \times 6 = (4 \times 6) + (4 \times 6)$
7   $6 \times \blacksquare = (6 \times 10) + (6 \times 4)$

57

1   Write this abacus number in words.
2   Add 2 to 1099.
3   What number must be added to eighty-eight to make one hundred and one?
4   Write the number that can replace $\blacksquare$ in $67 \times 6 = 6 \times \blacksquare$.
5   Write $>$, $<$ or $=$ in place of $\bullet$ in this number sentence.
       $3000 + 500 + 70 + 7 \; \bullet \; 3752$

6 Solve this equation (find the number that **n** stands for):

$$9 \times 9 = (9 \times 5) + (9 \times \mathbf{n}).$$

7 What fraction of this shape is coloured?

58

> We have already learned that a division can be written:
>
> $$3\overline{)\,27} \qquad \text{and} \qquad 27 \div 3.$$
>
> This division can also be written down like this: $\dfrac{27}{3}$
>
> This is known as the **fractional form**.

Remember the answer in division is called the **quotient**.
Find the quotients in these divisions.

1 $\dfrac{35}{5}$ 2 $\dfrac{42}{6}$ 3 $\dfrac{110}{10}$ 4 $\dfrac{100}{5}$

5 $\dfrac{500}{5}$ 6 $\dfrac{100}{20}$ 7 $\dfrac{32}{4}$

59

> We know that brackets tell us which part to work first.
> Sometimes, however, brackets are left out and we have to think of a
> rule to tell us what to do.
> The rule says that when there are no brackets we must always work
> out multiplication and division before addition and subtraction.

Complete each of these equations.

1 $6 + \frac{18}{3} - 4 = \blacksquare$ 2 $6 \times 8 - \frac{21}{3} = \blacksquare$

3 $20 - 4 \times 4 = \blacksquare$ 4 $(26 - 12) \times 2 = \blacksquare$

5 $6 \times (9 - 3) = \blacksquare$ 6 $4 + 2 \times 3 - 2 = \blacksquare$

7 $5 \times 6 - \frac{12}{3} = \blacksquare$

60

1 Divide 120 by 6.

2 Find a quarter of ninety-six.

3 How many fours are there in 60?

4 $\frac{18}{3} + \frac{25}{5} =$

5 $\frac{1}{3}$ of 102.

6 What is the remainder when 39 is divided by 5?

7 What fraction of this shape is coloured?

61

1 How many sevens are there in sixty-three?

2 Solve this equation: $\frac{14}{7} + \frac{\boldsymbol{n}}{7} = 7$.

3 What is $\frac{1}{7}$ of 56?

4 Use the number line below to help you solve this equation:

$$42 \div 7 = \boldsymbol{n}.$$

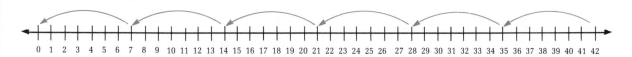

5 Study the subtractions below, then write out this equation in full:

$$35 \div \triangle = \blacksquare.$$

$$
\begin{array}{ccccc}
35 & 28 & 21 & 14 & 7 \\
-7 & -7 & -7 & -7 & -7 \\
\hline
28 & 21 & 14 & 7 & 0
\end{array}
$$

6 We can write two division facts for each multiplication fact, like this:

$$6 \times 7 = 42 \qquad 42 \div 7 = 6 \qquad 42 \div 6 = 7.$$

Write two division facts for $7 \times 3 = 21$.

7 What is the quotient when 70 is divided by 7?

62

1 Write down the greatest odd number that can be named with the three digits 4, 7 and 6.

2 Write out this statement in full:

$29 + 16 = \blacksquare + 6$

3 Take 50 from 5000.

4 Study this equation: $16 \times 17 = 272$.

   Now write out this equation in full: $272 \div 17 = \blacksquare$.

5 Look at this example: $4 + 4 + 4 + 4 = \blacksquare \rightarrow 4 \times 4 = 16$.

   Now write this equation as a multiplication.

   $$63 + 63 + 63 + 63 + 63 = \blacksquare.$$

6 Find $\frac{1}{3}$ of $(4 + 5) \times 2$.

7 Write a fraction to tell what part is black.

63

The Romans used seven main symbols to name numbers.

1	5	10	50	100	500	1000
I	V	X	L	C	D	M

To find the value of a number we must add the value of the numerals, like this:

XVIII $= 10 + 5 + 1 + 1 + 1 = 18$

CCXXXIII $= 100 + 100 + 10 + 10 + 10 + 1 + 1 + 1 = 233$

Write these in our numerals.

1 VIII   2 XVI   3 XXV   4 XXXII

5 Write fifteen in Roman numerals.

6 Write twenty in Roman numerals.

7 Write thirty-six in Roman numerals.

64

Now we can think about bigger numbers.

> **CCLXX** = 100 + 100 + 50 + 10 + 10 = 270
> **MDCCCIV** = 1000 + 500 + 100 + 100 + 100 + 4 = 1804

1 What is the value of LXX?

2 What is the value of CL?

3 What is the value of DCC?

4 What is the value of MDC?

5 What is the value of CXX?

6 What is the value of MMCCC?

7 What is the value of MMMDCCC?

65

> The Romans rarely used the same four symbols together.
> Instead of IIII for four they wrote IV (5 − 1).
> Instead of VIIII for nine they wrote IX (10 − 1).
> Instead of XXXX for forty they wrote XL (50 − 10).
> Instead of LXXXX for ninety they wrote XC (100 − 10).

1 Write in our numerals   XIV   {X + IV}

2 Write in our numerals   XXXIX   {XXX + IX}

3 Write in our numerals   CCXC   {CC + XC}

4 Write in our numerals   CXL   {C + XL}

5 Write nineteen in Roman numerals.

6 Write thirty-five in Roman numerals.

7 Write three hundred and forty in Roman numerals.

66

Work out the dates on these cornerstones.

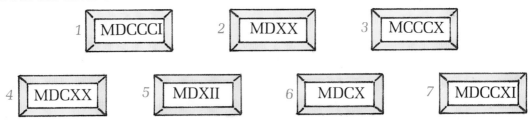

1 MDCCCI   *2* MDXX   *3* MCCCX

4 MDCXX   *5* MDXII   *6* MDCX   *7* MDCCXI

67

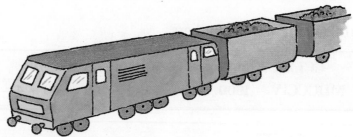

1 Write four thousand four hundred in digits.
2 Twice a certain number is 16. What is half the number?
3 A coal train carried a thousand tonnes of coal. Each wagon carried 20 tonnes.
  How many wagons were there?
4 What number is 7 more than the difference between 16 and 9?
5 When Sarah added 11 to a number, the answer was 23.
  What would have been her answer if she had subtracted 11?
6 Add a quarter of twelve to a third of fifteen.
7 Ali and Salim have twelve conkers altogether. Seven of these are Salim's.
  How many more has Salim than Ali?

68

Equations like the one below are really
number puzzles.

$$n + 3 = 7$$

It means **a certain number plus 3 equals 7.**

n stands for **a certain number**.

We have to find this number, and when we are trying
to find it we are trying to **solve** the equation.

Solve these equations.

1 $86 + n = 100$

2 $\frac{3}{4} + n = 1\frac{1}{4}$

3 $n + \frac{2}{3} = 1$

4 $n + 7\frac{1}{2} = 15$

5 $4\frac{1}{2} + n = 7$

6 $n + 11 = 50$

7 $n + 63 + 17 = 120$

69

Remember we can use any letter or other symbol like 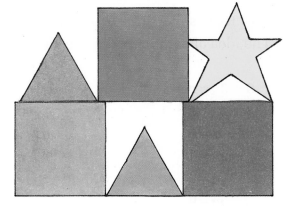 or ★
or ▲ to stand for a number.

Solve these equations.

1 $\triangle - 14 = 16$ 2 $23 - n = 13$

3 $\bigstar - 25 = 75$ 4 $100 - \blacksquare = 89$

5 $x - \frac{3}{4} = \frac{1}{4}$ 6 $\frac{3}{4} - n = \frac{1}{2}$

7 $z - 12 = 18$

70

When we use letters in place of numbers we can show
multiplication without using the multiplication sign ($\times$).

$$3b \text{ means } 3 \times b \left\{ \begin{array}{c} \text{3 multiplied by a certain number} \\ \text{or} \\ \text{3 times a certain number} \end{array} \right\}$$

Solve these equations. If you wish, you can work out the equation in your book
using the multiplication sign.

$$4n = 12 \qquad 4 \times n = 12$$

1 $6n = 30$ 2 $2a = 150$

3 $3n = 21$ 4 $20x = 100$

5 $50 = 5x$ 6 $1000 = 10x$

7 $63 = 7n$

71

$$6 + 3 \quad = \quad n + 1$$

Now try to solve these equations.

The idea of **balancing** the two sides can be helpful.

1 $6 + 3 = n + 1$ 2 $6 + 7 = a - 2$

3 $3 + n = 8 - 3$ 4 $1 + 4 = y - 1$

5 $m + n = 6$ 6 $m - n = 4$

    $m = 4$ $m = 7$

    $n = ?$ $n = ?$

7     $m = 9$

  $m + n = 17$

     $n = ?$

72

1 What is the greatest number you can name with the digits 3, 1, 4 and 2?

2 How many tens are there in five hundred?

3 What is $\frac{3}{4}$ of 24?

4 Solve this equation: $\frac{35}{7} + x = 12$.

5 How many pencils are needed to give 24 boys and 16 girls two pencils each?

6 Think of the number 11. Add 9 to it. Double it. Find a fifth.

What is the answer?

7 At a school swimming gala there were 90 divers.

A third of the divers were boys. How many divers were girls?

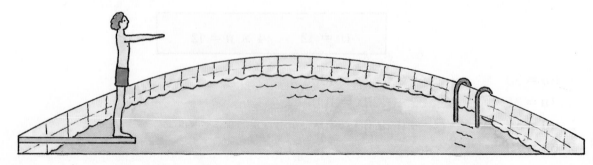

73

1 Find the product of 5 and 8.
2 One-eighth of a number is 4. What is the number?
3 Divide thirty-two by eight.
4 Multiply eight by itself.
5 How many eights are in eighty?
6 Eight girls shared 72 beads equally.
   How many did each girl get?
7 A lorry driver works forty hours a week.
   If he works eight hours a day, how
   many days does he work each week?

74

1 If I divide a number by 8, the quotient is 6.
   What is the number?
2 Find $\frac{1}{8}$ of 64.
3 How many are seven eights?
4 How many children can each be given an orange from a box which has
   eight rows and nine oranges in each row?
5 Solve this equation: $\frac{32}{8} = a$.
6 What fraction of this shape is coloured?

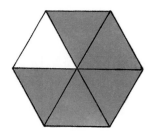

7 A class has eight full boxes of crayons. There are eighty-eight crayons
   altogether. How many are there in the box?

75

1 How many nines are in 72?
2 The product of two numbers is 99. One number is 9.
   What is the other number?
3 Solve $r \times 7 = 63$.

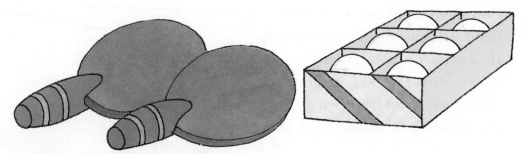

4 How many table tennis balls are there in nine full boxes?
5 A total of 81 dots is arranged so that there is an equal number in each row.
   How many are there in a row?
6 David has 36p. Apples are 9p each. How many can he buy?
7 When a number was divided by 9, the quotient was 3.
   What was the number?

76

1 Mala has nine pages of foreign stamps and nine stamps on each page.
   How many stamps has she?

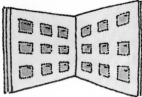

2 Find $\frac{1}{9}$ of 45.
3 What number when multiplied by 9 is 8 less than 80?
4 Take nine times 0 from nine times 10.
5 Add the product of 4 and 9 to the product of 2 and 9.
6 Solve $\frac{z}{9} + 1 = 10$
7 One-ninth of the children in Class 3 have red hair.
   There are three red-heads. How many children are in the class?

77

1 Write in words the number which is ten less than a thousand.

2 Three-quarters of the distance between two villages is fifteen kilometres.
How many kilometres apart are the villages?

3 Lisa's pencil case holds twenty-four pencils. She has four blue pencils,
five red and seven green. The rest are yellow. What fraction (part) of the pencils
is yellow?

4 Find $\frac{1}{3}$ of the difference between 32 and 50.

5 Each reel in the picture below holds 100 metres of thread.
How many metres of thread are there altogether on all the reels?

6 Find the sum: 89 + 67 + 11.

7 What number is 7 more than the product of 7 and 8?

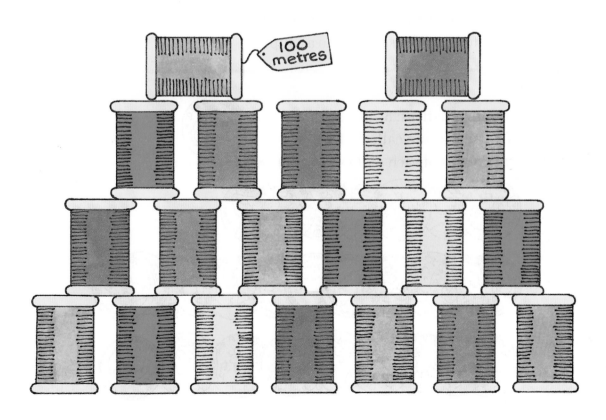

78

Practise counting in tens: 10, 20, 30, 40 . . .
Here is a ten pence coin called a **ten**.
Find the total value of each of these rows of coins.

1

2

3

4 How many tens are the same value as 80p?

5 How many tens are the same value as 30p?

6 How many tens are the same value as 60p?

7 How many tens are the same value as 40p?

79

Practise counting in fives: 5, 10, 15, 20 . . .
Here is a five pence coin called a **five**.
Find the total value of each of these rows of coins.

4 How many fives are the same value as 20p?

5 How many fives are the same value as 70p?

6 How many fives are the same value as 85p?

7 How many fives are the same value as 45p?

80

Practise counting in twos: 2, 4, 6, 8 . . .

Here is a two pence coin called a **two**.

Find the total value of each of these rows of coins.

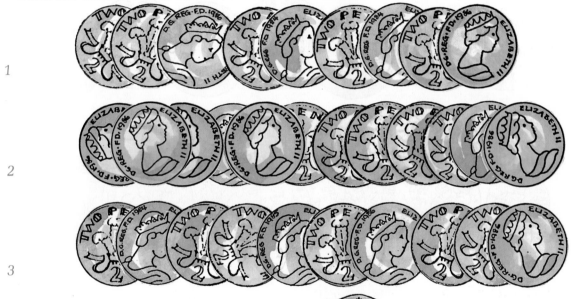

1

2

3

Here is a twenty pence coin called a twenty.

Find the value of this row.

4

5 How many twos are equal in value to 30p?

6 How many twos are equal in value to 64p?

7 How many twenties are equal in value to 60p?

81

Find the total value of the coins in each of these rows.

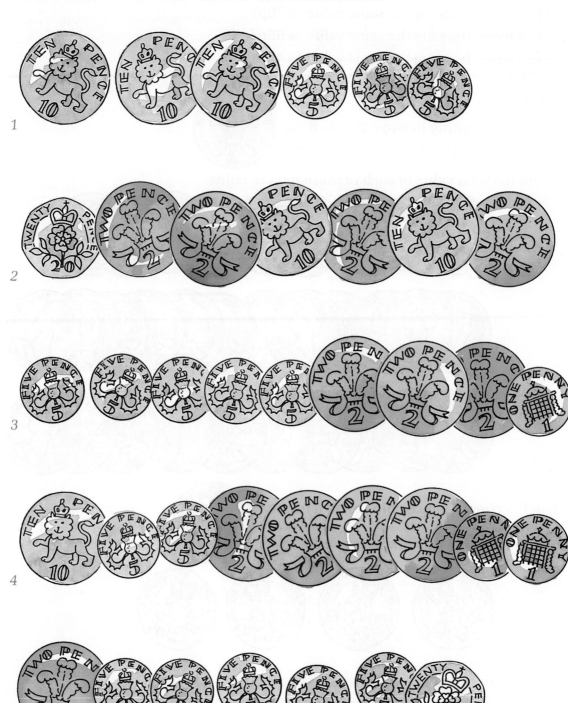

1

2

3

4

5

6

7

82

1 A village school had five classes with thirty children in each class.
   How many children were in the school?

2 These pupils went on a school visit in 3 coaches.
   There were the same number of pupils in each coach.
   How many were in each coach?

3 A quarter of Class 4 have their swimming badge.
   There are twenty-eight pupils in the class.
   How many have not?

4 Emma has 25 shells and Karen 15. If all their shells were put into
   4 equal groups, how many would be in each group?

5 When a certain number was divided by 3,
   the quotient was 5 and the remainder 2. What was the number?

6 Solve this equation: $\frac{500}{2} - x = 240$.

7 Next year Raj will be half his uncle's age. His uncle is 31 years old now.
   How old is Raj?

83

1 For which coin could you exchange these pennies?

How many fives are equal in value to each of the following?

2 3 twenties   *3* 6 tens   *4* 10 twos

How many tens are equal in value to each
of the following?

5 8 fives   *6* 90 pennies   *7* 4 twenties

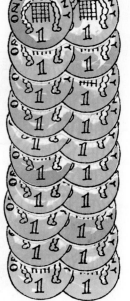

84

How many pence are equal in value to each of these?

1 1 ten, 1 five and 1 two

2 2 tens and 1 five

3 7 tens and 4 twos

4 3 tens, 1 five and 2 twos

5 8 tens, 1 five and 2 twos

6 7 tens and 3 pennies

7 four twenties and four pennies

85

How many pence are equal in value to each of these?

1 1 ten and 3 fives

2 4 fives and 10 pennies

3 2 twenties, 2 fives and 2 twos

4 3 tens and 5 fives

5 1 ten, 4 fives and 7 pennies

6 1 twenty, 5 fives and 4 pennies

7 1 ten, 5 twos and 6 pennies

86

Put the correct number in place of each ■.

1 49p = ■ fives and 2 twos.

2 83p = ■ tens and 3 pennies.

3 91p = ■ twenties, 2 fives and 1 penny.

4 25p = ■ fives, 2 twos and 1 penny.

5 50p = 3 tens, 2 fives and ■ twos.

6 27p = 1 ten and ■ pennies.

7 73p = 2 twenties, ■ fives and 3 pennies.

87

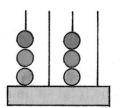

1 Write in words the number shown on the abacus.

2 Write out the equation below in full.

$7 \times (6 \times 0) = $ ■

3 Write out the numbers below in order of size
   from the least to the greatest.

   4400   4044   4004   4040

4 Copy, and write > or < or = in place of ⬤.

   600 + 70 + 8 ⬤ 786

5 Copy, and write > or < in place of ⬤.

   XXIX ⬤ XXXI

6 What fraction of the dogs is black?

7 When I subtract 6 and 19 from a certain number,
   I get 15. What is the number?

88

Here is a fifty pence coin called a **fifty**.

1 How many fives are equal in value to a fifty?

2 How many fives are equal in value to 4 fifties?

3 How many tens can be exchanged for 6 fifties?

4 How many twos are equal in value to a fifty?

5 How many twenties are equal to 4 fifties?

6 What are the missing coins?

$$50p = 20p + 5p + \blacksquare p + \triangle p$$

7 What is the total value in pence of the coins shown above?

89

100 pence make 1 pound.
We can write **1 pound** as **£1** or **£1·00**.
£1·00 means **1 pound and no pence**.
£1·43 means **1 pound and 43 pence**.

Write these amounts in pounds and pence.

1 £4·86 means ■ pounds and ▲ pence.

2 £3·40 means ■ pounds and ▲ pence.

3 £6·39 means ■ pounds and ▲ pence.

4 £2·05 means ■ pounds and ▲ pence.

5 £7·23 means ■ pounds and ▲ pence.

6 £10·03 means ■ pounds and ▲ pence.

7 £13·70 means ■ pounds and ▲ pence.

90

> £9·63 means 9 pounds and 63 pence.
> We say **nine pounds sixty-three.**

Write these amounts using the £ sign.

1 three pounds twenty-three
2 seven pounds eighty
3 twenty pounds seventeen
4 eight pounds five
5 two pounds twenty
6 six pounds fifty-five
7 ten pounds ten

91

£7·45   **seven pounds forty-five**

Write the amounts on these labels in words.

1 £6·69

2 £14·40

3 £30·07

4 £5·15

5 £7·04

6 £9·90

7 £20·00

92

1 Write five thousand five hundred and fifty in digits.

2 Round off this calculator number to the nearest thousand.

3 Write down the letter of each number sentence which is true.

a $17 + 6 = 30 - 7$ b $6 \times 8 = 6 \times 7 + 1$

c $130 - 37 = 100 - 7$ d $4 \times 5 = 5 \times 4$

4 Find the product of 2, 6 and 25.

5 Sam and Emma shared equally two packets of chocolate buttons.
The first packet held 23 and the second 29. How many did each have?

6 While playing darts, David scored 3, 6 and 9. Peter scored 7, 5 and 2.
How many more did David score?

7 What fraction of this circle is red?

93

> We can write amounts of money less than a pound in two ways:
>
>   with a pound sign   with a pence sign
>
>   £0·39   £0·03   39p   3p
>
> We always place a nought in the £ column when the amount
> is less than £1, like this: £0·67.

Use the pound sign (£) to write these amounts.

1 forty-nine pence   2 six pence

3 ninety pence   4 eighty-three pence

5 seventeen pence

6

7

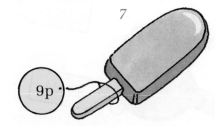

94

£4·83 = (400 + 80 + 3) pence

Now write out these in the same way.

1 £4·65 = (400 + ■ + 5) pence
2 £7·80 = (700 + ■) pence
3 £9·06 = (900 + ■) pence
4 £3·24 = (■ + 20 + 4) pence
5 £7·00 = ■ p
6 £4·09 = ■ p
7 £3·70 = ■ p

95

Change these amounts of pence to pounds and pence,
like this:

p	£
460	4·60

1 367p
2 409p
3 835p
4 770p
5 600p
6 803p
7 919p

96

1 How many pennies are equal in value to £1·00?
2 How many pennies are equal in value to £1·10?
3 How many pennies are equal in value to £1·01?
4 How many pennies are equal in value to £1·11?
5 Which coin is the same value as £0·02?
6 Which coin is the same value as £0·20?
7 Which coin is the same value as £0·50?

97

> We have learned that we can add numbers in any order we like.

1 Remember this useful law when adding these numbers.

   $17 + 16 + 3 + 4 = \blacksquare$

2 How many tens are there in two hundred and ten?

3 Add 6×7 and 4×7.

4 $(\frac{1}{5} \text{ of } 100) + (\frac{1}{4} \text{ of } 20) = \blacksquare$.

5 An ice rink has seats for 1500 spectators.

   How many spectators are there when it is half full?

6 For our school visit to Windsor Castle we had 5 coaches.

   Each coach carried 38 pupils and 2 teachers.

   How many people went on the visit?

7 This graph shows the number of pets owned by pupils in a class.
   a How many more dogs are owned than cats?
   b How many pets are owned altogether?

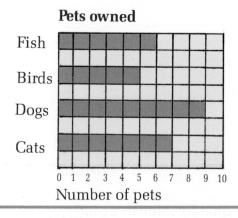

Pets owned

Number of pets

98

1 How many tens are equal in value to £1·20?

2 How many tens are equal in value to £3·00?

3 How many tens are equal in value to £6·70?

4 Change 14 tens to pounds and pence.

5 Change 11 tens to pounds and pence.

6 Change 20 tens to pounds and pence.

7 Change 38 tens to pounds and pence.

is worth

99

1. How many fives are equal in value to 35p?
2. How many fives are equal in value to £0·45?
3. How many fives are equal in value to £1·50?
4. How many fives are equal in value to £2·00?
5. How many fives are equal in value to £2·50?
6. Change 60 fives to pounds and pence.
7. Change 22 fives to pounds and pence.

is worth

100

 is worth  or

1. How many twos are equal in value to 32p?
2. How many twos are equal in value to £0·60p?
3. How many twenties are equal in value to £5·00?
4. How many twenties are equal in value to £1·20?
5. Change 80 twos to pounds and pence.
6. Change 75 twos to pounds and pence.
7. Change 9 twenties to pounds and pence.

101

1. How many fifties are equal in value to £2·50?
2. How many fifties are equal in value to £4·00?
3. How many fifties are equal in value to £7·50?
4. How many fifties are equal in value to £50·00
5. Change 3 fifties to pounds and pence.
6. Change 6 fifties to pounds.
7. Change 10 fifties to pounds.

102

1. Write in words the number which is two less than a thousand.
2. Find one-sixth of the product of four and nine.
3. Find the sum of the even numbers in the box.
4. Half a certain number is equal to one-third of twelve. What is the number?
5. Simon had £5 in the bank. He took out £1·35 and then £1·15. How much did he have left?
6. If I shared 100 apples equally among 4 boys and 6 girls, how many apples would each have?
7. What fraction of the dots is blue?

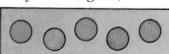

103

Find the cost of:

1 12 beads at 4 for 1p.   2 8 beads at 2 for 3p.

3 16 beads at 4 for 3p.   4 20 beads at 5 for 2p.

5 4 beads at 2 for 7p.   6 27 beads at 9 for 5p.

7 36 beads at 4 for 7p.

104

1 Pencils cost 9p each. How many can be bought for £1·80?

2 Paint brushes cost 40p each. How many can be bought for £2·00?

3 Rolls of tape are 30p each. How many can be bought for £2·10?

4 How many coloured pens at 25p each can be bought for £4?

5 Crayons cost 8p each. How many can be bought for 56p?

6 A pair of scissors costs 50p. How many pairs can be bought for £5?

7 How many felt pens at 40p each can be bought with 6 twenties?

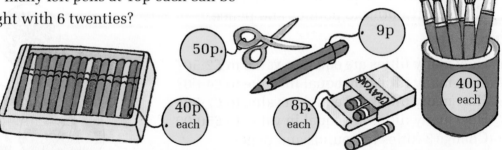

105

1 How many ballpoint pens at 30p each can be bought for £1·20?

2 How many diaries at 90p each can be bought for £1·80?

3 How many scrap books at 50p each can be bought for £4·50?

4 How many pocket dictionaries at 60p each can be bought for £2·40?

5 How many wallets at 90p each can be bought for £9·00?

6 How many notebooks at 40p each can be bought for £2·00?

7 How many desk kits at 70p each can be bought for £2·80?

106

1 Rashmi spent 20p on crayons at 3 for 10p.
How many did she buy?

2 Ginger biscuits are 3 for 2p. How many
can be bought with a ten?

3 How many chocolate fingers can be bought
with a twenty, if they are 3 for 5p?

4 If envelopes are 4 for 11p, how many
can be bought for 55p?

5 Marbles are 5 for 3p. How many can be bought for 24p?

6 How many glass beads can be bought for 36p,
if they cost 9p for 5?

7 A lady spent 30p on coloured laces. If they were 3
for 10p, how many did she buy?

107

1 How many times greater than sixty is six thousand?

2 Find the sum of the odd numbers between 4 and 8.

3 Paul had 300 picture stickers. He put 5 on each
page of his album. How many pages did he fill?

4 Re-arrange the numbers below in order of size
from the least to the greatest.

5 Look how these numbers grow. Write the
next two numbers.

    4360,   4370,   4380,   4390,   ?,   ?

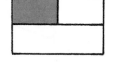

6 What fraction of the shape on the right is red?

7 Oranges are 17p each. How many can I buy for £1·70?

108

1 How much money would you need to pay
   for a bottle of raspberryade at 17p, a packet
   of potato crisps at 12p and a candy bar at 18p?
2 What is the sum of 18p, 12p and 9p?
3 Work out the total cost of a packet of hazelnuts
   at 65p a packet, a packet of walnuts at 99p a packet
   and a packet of peanuts and raisins at 35p a packet.
4 Peter spent 60p, 85p and 40p.
   How much did he spend altogether?
5 Add 9p, 36p and 4p.
6 Sue paid 25p each for 2 comics and her mother paid 25p each for 2 magazines.
   How much did they pay in all?
7 Find the total of 13p, 19p, 7p and 1p.

109

Find these totals.

1 £0·36 + £0·06 = £ ▲
2 £0·40 + £0·03 = £ ◆
3 £0·48 + £0·02 = £ ◆
4 £0·26 + £0·33 = £ ▣
5 £0·27 + £0·33 = £ ▣
6 £0·16 + £0·48 = £ ▲
7 £0·73 + £0·20 = £ ▲

110

Find these totals.

1 76p + 8p = £ ▣
2 40p + 56p = £ ◆
3 34p + 55p = £ ▲
4 68p + 22p = £ ▲

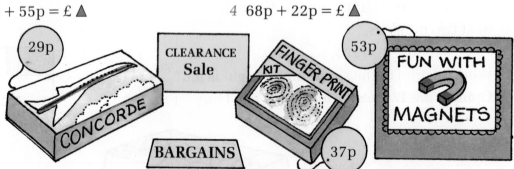

5 What is the total cost of the Concorde Kit and the Fingerprint Kit?
6 How much must be paid for the Fun with Magnets and the Fingerprint Kit?
7 Find the total cost of the Fun with Magnets and the Concorde Kit.

111

> When an answer is 100p or more,
> change it to pounds and pence, like this:
> 40p + 16p + 63p = £1·19.

1 What is the total cost of *Pictorial Science* and *True Stories*?

2 How much would be paid for *Pictorial Science* and *Space Travel*?

Find these totals.

3 80p + 60p = £ ▢   4 96p + 80p = £ ▲

5 90p + 70p = £ ▲   6 40p + 30p + 50p = £ ▢

7 40p + 85p = £ ◆

112

1 Write the number eight thousand in digits.

2 How many kilometres is it from DIN to NID?

3 Jason won 40 conkers yesterday and twice as many the day before. How many has he won altogether?

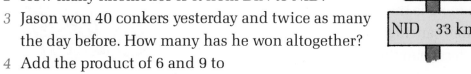

4 Add the product of 6 and 9 to the difference between 6 and 9.

5 Solve this equation: $4x = \frac{32}{8}$

Twenty children were asked which fruit they preferred — an apple or a banana.

6 How many preferred an apple?

7 How many preferred a banana?

113

Find these totals.

1 £0·60 + £0·70 = £ ▢   2 £3·40 + £2·90 = £ ▲

3 £0·90 + £0·80 = £ ◆   4 £5·63 + £1·07 = £ ▢

5 £0·42 + £0·70 = £ ▲   6 £1·65 + £0·35 = £ ◆

7 £0·63 + £0·37 = £ ▢

114

1 What change would I have from a fifty after
buying a notebook and a pencil?
2 Take 7p from 70p.
3 How much less than 40p is 17p?
4 What is left when 28p is taken from 80p?
5 What must be added to 63p to make 90p?
6 Subtract 14p from 23p.
7 If Usha had another 13p, she would have 65p.
How much does she have now?

115

Find the differences between these amounts.

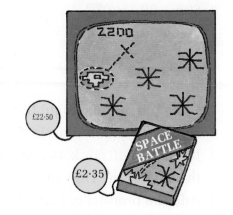

1 £0·69 − £0·07 = £ ▢
2 £0·80 − £0·63 = £ ▢
3 £0·94 − £0·30 = £ ▢
4 £0·45 − £0·23 = £ ▢
5 £0·40 − £0·33 = £ ▢
6 How much more is the video game
than the game cartridge?
7 How much less than the football
is the game cartridge?

116

Find the differences between these amounts.

1 £1·50 − £0·75 = £ ▢   2 £1·20 − £0·25 = £ ▢
3 £1·40 − £0·60 = £ ▲   4 £2·50 − £1·30 = £ ▲
5 £1·60 − 90p = £ ◆   6 £1·10 − £0·70p = £ ◆
7 £1·35 − 40p = £ ▢

117

1 >, < or = ? Write the correct sign in place of ⬤

$$4 \times 6 \;\bigcirc\; 31 - 6$$

2 Copy, and write the missing sign $(+, -, \times, \div)$ in place of each ⬤

$$16 \;\bigcirc\; 2 = 4 \;\bigcirc\; 2$$

3 If I add a number to itself, then add 7, I get 15. What is the number?

4 Find the sum of 35, 26 and 35.

5 How much change did Nina have from £10 after buying a pencil, a ball and a book?

6 How long will it take Sharon to save £2·50, if she saves 50p a week?

7 What change would I have from a £10 note after spending £6·70?

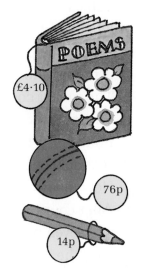

POEMS £4·10
76p
14p

118

How much change would you have if you spend:

1 £0·30 out of £1·00?   2 £1·50 out of £10?

3 45p out of £1·00?   4 £0·20 out of £20?

5 £0·69 out of £1·00?   6 £5·50 out of £50·00?

7 £0·40 out of £5·00?

119

1 How much less than a fifty is 9p plus 6p?

2 What must be added to 58p to make a pound?

3 The cheapest fountain-pen in a shop is £1·50 and the dearest is £20·00. What is the difference in price?

4 Lisa has already paid 70p towards the cost of a school visit. If the total cost of the visit is £7, how much more has she to pay?

5 Three boys clubbed together for a football costing £15. Kevin paid £5·20 and Michael £5·30. How much did Peter pay?

6 Four twenties were handed to a shopkeeper in payment for a magazine costing 65p. How much change did the shopkeeper give to the customer?

7 How many fives are equal in value to the total of 8p, 7p, 4p and 6p?

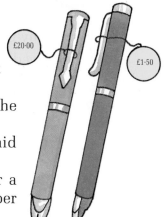

£20·00
£1·50

120

1 Baby Jane's piggy-bank holds 27p. There are
  3 fives and the rest of the coins are pennies.
  How many pennies are there?
2 A rubber and a pencil cost 60p.
  The rubber costs 48p. What is the cost of the pencil?
3 Mr Green received a ten and 3 fives change
  from a fifty. How much had he spent in the shop?

4 A shopkeeper went to the bank for £3·10 in tens.
  How many coins was she given?
5 After counting her money, a woman found she
  was seven pence short of £2. How much did she have?
6 Find the difference between £2·80 and £3·50.
7 Sarah wants a book costing £5·00. How long
  will it take her to save the money, if she puts away 20p
  each week?

121

1 What is the total of 80p and £2·40?
2 How much change did Claire have from £1 after
  buying a tube of toothpaste and a toothbrush?
3 Jaswant has saved 60p. Mohammed has saved twice
  as much. How much in pounds and pence have
  they saved altogether?

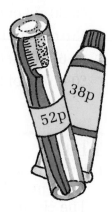

4 How many peaches at 20p each can you buy for £1·40?
5 Karen saved £3·85 for school camp. Then her father gave her
  £2·50 and her mother £5·50. How much did she have in
  pounds and pence?

6 A shopkeeper gave 34p change in twos.
How many coins did she hand to the customer?

7 How much change would I have from £1
after buying twenty 4p balloons?

122

1 What number is 101 more than 7689?

2 In our school hall there are 54 chairs in 6 equal rows.
How many chairs are there in a row?

3 A hundred and twenty eggs are packed a dozen
in a box. How many full boxes are there?

4 Find the difference between the sum and
product of 5 and 6.

5 How many twos are equal in value to 8 fives?

6 Rani bought a second-hand bicycle for £24·75 and a
new bell for £1·25. How much did she pay altogether?

7 A club went on an outing. If the total cost of the coach trip
was £50 and the fare was 50p each,
how many went?

123

What is the value of:

1 the pennies?

2 the twos?

3 the fives?

4 the tens?

5 the twenties?

6 the fifties?

7 the twos and
fives together?

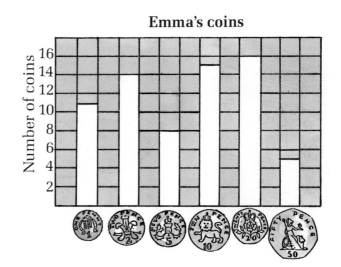

Emma's coins

124

Find the cost of:

1 2 orange fruities at 25p each.
2 2 double choc ices at 35p each.
3 2 strawberry splits at 26p each.
4 2 ice-cream tubs at 29p each.
5 2 king cones at 37p each.
6 2 raspberry ripples at 46p each.
7 2 choc-cherry slices at 38p each.

125

When an answer is 100p or more, change it to pounds and pence, like this: £1·53.

Find the cost of:

1 2 pocket dictionaries at 70p each.
2 4 pairs of scissors at 90p each.
3 2 notebooks at 55p each.
4 6 rulers at 80p each.
5 7 diaries at 70p each.
6 5 erasers at 30p each.
7 6 drawing books at 25p each.

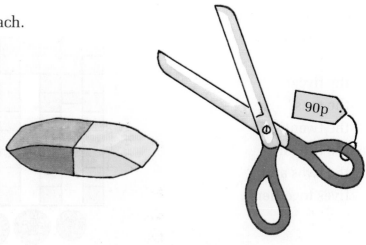

126

Find the cost of:

1 2 tennis rackets at £20·25 each.
2 3 sports bags at £9·30 each.
3 4 table tennis sets at £5·40 each.
4 2 boomerangs at £2·99 each.
5 7 rounders sets (bat and ball) at £4·20 a set.
6 3 scrambling nets at £11·50 each.
7 5 rope ladders at £7·40 each.

127

1 How many of these small cubes are there in the large cube?
2 A lorry driver travelled 47 km on Monday
   and 63 km on Tuesday. How many kilometres
   altogether did he travel on the two days?
3 Susan put 8 stamps on each of the 6 pages of her
   stamp album. She also had 12 stamps in an
   envelope. How many stamps did she have in all?

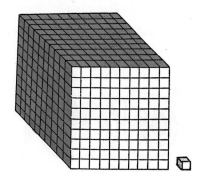

4 What fraction of the green plates is cracked?
5 What fraction of all the plates is cracked?
6 Katy bought 2 bananas for 15p each and gave the
   exact money. Which two coins did she give?
7 A bank changed £5 to fives.
   How many coins were there?

128

1 7 apples cost 63p. What is the cost of 1?
2 3 oranges cost 45p. What is the cost of 1?
3 2 pears cost 32p. What is the cost of 1?
4 4 tomatoes cost 36p. What is the cost of 1?
5 4 lemons cost 48p. What is the cost of 1?
6 5 peaches cost £1.
   What is the cost of 1?
7 4 melons cost £2.
   What is the cost of 1?

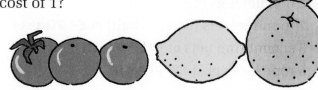

129

1 What is the cost of 1 funny face mask, if 8 cost £4?
2 What is the cost of 1 horror mask, if 5 cost £2?
3 What is the cost of 1 gorilla mask, if 4 cost £6?
4 What is the cost of 1 carnival mask, if 10 cost £2?
5 What is the cost of 1 carnival hat, if 10 cost £5?
6 What is the cost of 1 set of modelling balloons, if 10 sets cost £4?
7 What is the cost of 1 set of giant balloons, if 5 sets cost £1·50?

130

1 10 squeaker balloons cost 80p. What is the cost of 1?
2 20 blow-outs cost £1. What is the cost of 1?
3 100 streamers cost £2. What is the cost of 1?
4 10 tree decorations cost £1·50. What is the cost of 1?
5 12 giant crackers cost £6. What is the cost of 1?
6 2 reels of Christmas ribbon cost £1·10. What is the cost of 1?
7 8 sheets of gift wrap cost £2. What is the cost of 1?

131

Write these answers using the £ sign.

1 What is the cost of 1 hang glider, if 2 cost £1·60?
2 Divide £2·50 by 5.
3 Share £2·10 equally among 7 people.
4 What is a quarter of £3·60?
5 £4·16 ÷ 4 = £
6 If £4·20 was shared equally among Usha and her two friends, how much would each girl have?
7 Find half of £7·20.

132

1 Write in digits the number that is 500 more than 9506.
2 The distance from London to Edinburgh by rail is approximately 630 kilometres. What is the approximate distance from London to Edinburgh and back?
3 In a school dining-room two hundred and ninety pupils have dinner and sit ten to a table. How many full tables are there?
4 Mr Robb drove his car at an average speed of 50 kilometres per hour for $2\frac{1}{2}$ hours. What distance did he travel?
5 Andrew had 483 marbles and 11 bags. He placed 40 marbles in each bag. How many marbles were left over?
6 Look at the graph. How many trees were planted altogether?
7 Find the difference between £10·10 and £10·01.

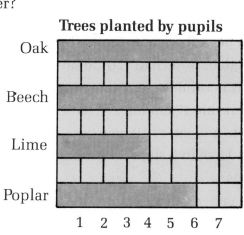

Trees planted by pupils

Oak · Beech · Lime · Poplar

1 2 3 4 5 6 7
Number

133

These are **centimetre** lengths.

1 cm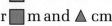

10 cm

100 cm = 1 metre (m)

Bob's height is **118 cm** or **1 m and 18 cm.**

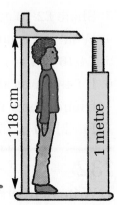

118 cm   1 metre

Now try these.

1   400 cm or ▢ m

2   190 cm or ▢ m and ▲ cm

3   600 cm or ▢ m

4   335 cm or ▢ m and ▲ cm

5   490 cm or ▢ m and ▲ cm

6   788 cm or ▢ m and ▲ cm

7   1000 cm or ▢ m

134

Find the cost of:

1   3 metres at 70p a metre.

2   50 cm at 30p a metre.

3   25 cm at 8p a metre.

4   20 cm at 5p a metre.

5   70 cm at £1 a metre.

6   4 m and 50 cm at 6p a metre.

7   1 m and 3 cm at £1 a metre.

135

1   I gave £2 for 2 metres of silver wire. How much would a centimetre of wire cost?

2   A length of first-aid dressing was cut into 3 equal lengths, each 90 cm.
    What had been the whole length in m and cm?

3   A 5 m length of wood had 120 cm sawn off. What length in m and cm remained?

4   How many centimetres are there in $1\frac{1}{4}$ m?

5   New pencils are 17 cm long. What is the total
    length in m and cm of 10 new pencils?

6   John goes $1\frac{1}{2}$ m in 3 steps. How long in cm is each
    of his steps?

7   A strip of paper 1 m and 10 cm long is folded in the
    middle. What is the length of each half?

136

Longer distances are measured in **metres** and **kilometres.**

> **1 kilometre (1 km) = 1000 metres**

The distance from Tipton to Stanton is
2 km and **700 m** or **2700 m**.

Now try these.

1 1900 m =  km and ▲ m
2 3000 m = ■ km
3 4630 m = ■ km and ▲ m
4 7500 m = ■ km and ▲ m
5 6 km = ■ m
6 1 km and 376 m = ■ m
7 ■ m + 890 m = 1 km

PARIS
10 km

ZOO
ENTRANCE

200 m

250 m

137

Solve these equations by finding the number which can replace ■ in each.

1 1 km − 750 m = ■ m
2 400 m x 5 = ■ km
3 1700 m + 2300 m = ■ km
4 5 km − 1000 m = ■ m
5 400 m + ■ m = 1 km
6 1500 m + ■ m = 2 km
7 ■ m + 90 m = 1 km

138

1 Write nine thousand and nineteen in digits.

2 Find one-third of the product of eight and nine.

3 25 x 5 x 2 x 2 = ■

4 9 metres of ribbon cost 45p. What did 1 metre cost?

1 DOZEN EGGS

5 This was a full box of eggs. What fraction of the eggs is still in the box?

6 Arrange these lengths in order of size, starting with the smallest.

$$4\frac{1}{4} \text{ metres} \qquad 440 \text{ centimetres} \qquad 4 \text{ m } 4 \text{ cm}$$

7 What length (in metres) of plastic edging was needed for this square coffee table?

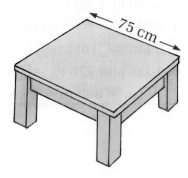

75 cm

139

1000 grams = 1 kilogram (kg)

A parcel weighs **5 kg** and **300 g** or **5300 g.**

Now try these.

1 How many grams are there in 2 kg and 200 g?

2 How many grams are there in $\frac{1}{10}$ kg?

3 Change 9 kg and 900 g to grams.

4 Change $2\frac{1}{2}$ kg to grams.

5 Find the number of grams in $1\frac{3}{4}$ kg.

6 Change 8 kg and 80 g to grams.

7 How many grams are there in 9 kg and 9 g?

140

1 Write in digits the number which is five hundred and five more than five thousand.

2 Write out this addition in full:

$$\begin{array}{r} \blacksquare\,\blacksquare\,\blacksquare \\ +\ 6\ 0\ 2 \\ \hline 8\ 0\ 1 \\ \hline \end{array}$$

3 Solve this equation: $350 + 550 = 1000 - n$.

4 Which sign $(+, -, \times \text{ or } \div)$ should be placed instead of $\blacksquare$ in this equation?
$$305 + 295 = 550 \ \blacksquare \ 50$$

5 What is the total cost of 10 slices of custard tart and 10 glasses of milk?

6 How many centimetres are there in $10\frac{1}{2}$ metres?

7 $1400\text{ m} + \blacksquare = 1\frac{1}{2}\text{ km}$

141

1 How many kilograms are there in 5500 grams?

2 Change 8070 g to kg and g.

3 Change 4750 g to kg.

4 How many kg and g are there in 1001 g?

5 Change 6606 g to kg and g.

6 How many $\frac{1}{2}$ kg are there in 2500 g?

7 How many 250 g packets of butter weigh $2\frac{1}{2}$ kg?

142

Solve these equations. Write the answers only.

1 9 kg and 200 g = ☐ g

2 450 g + ☐ g = $\frac{1}{2}$ kg

3 760 g + ☐ g = 1 kg

4 800 g + ☐ g = 2 kg

5 3 kg − 1900 g = ☐ g

6 5 kg − $\frac{1}{2}$ kg = ☐ g

7 2 kg 500 g − 900 g = ☐ g

143

1 What is the total weight in kg and g of the bag of chips and the packet of crisps?

2 300 g + 500 g + 600 g = ? kg and ? g

3 600 g + 900 g + 400 g = ? kg and ? g

4 1 kg and 700 g + 2 kg and 600 g = ? kg and ? g

5 Add and bring to kg and g: $\frac{1}{2}$ kg and 600 g

6 $3\frac{1}{2}$ kg + 400 g = ? kg and ? g

7 800 g + 300 g + 700 g + 200 g = ? kg

Potato Chips

980 g

Potato Crisps

40 g

144

1 Take $\frac{1}{2}$ kg from 700 g.

2 Subtract 700 grams from 1 kg and 300 g.

3 Find the difference between 1 kg 700 g and 900 g.

4 How many grams are left when 1 kg and 400 g are taken from 2 kg?

5 How many grams must be added to 1 kg and 900 g to make 3 kg?

6 From 5 kg take 1 kg and 100 g.

7 What is the difference in kg and g between 4 kilograms and 400 grams?

145

1 Write ten thousand and ten in digits.
2 The sum of three numbers is a thousand.
   The numbers are 340, 160 and ■
3 How much change would you have from a £10 note
   if you spent £1·10?
4 In a collection box there were one hundred
   and one pennies. Write this in pounds and pence.
5 What fraction of the shapes on the right is green?
6 A cyclist travelled 60 kilometres in 4 hours. If she
   kept up the same speed all the time, how far
   did she cycle in 1 hour?
7 Mark covers 50 centimetres in one step.
   How many metres will he cover in 40 steps?

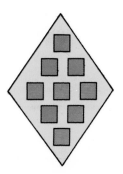

146

1 Shubi's schoolbag weighed 8 kg. She took out a
   dictionary weighing 800 g. What was the
   weight of her schoolbag then?
2 4 apples weigh 500 g. How many apples of the
   same size weigh $1\frac{1}{2}$ kg?
3 Six chocolates weigh 100 grams. How many are
   there in a box holding 1 kilogram of chocolates?
4 A fruit cake was cut into quarters.
   If each share weighed 400 g, what was
   the weight of the whole cake in kg and g?
5 How many 200-gram packets of lemonade powder
   can be made up from a tin holding 2 kilograms?
6 Ten biscuits weigh 50 g. How many are there
   in a box holding half a kilogram?
7 How many 10-gram weights are needed to
   balance $\frac{1}{4}$ kilogram?

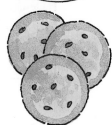

147

Find the cost of:

1 $\frac{1}{2}$ kg at 6p for 100 g.

2 $1\frac{1}{2}$ kg at 4p for 500 g.

3 750 g at 16p per kg.

4 100 g at 10p per kg.

5 1 kg 500 g at 6p per kg.

6 900 g at 10p per kg.

7 250 g at 12p per kg.

148

The **litre** is the basic measurement for liquid.

We write ℓ for litre.

The **millilitre (ml)** is used to measure smaller amounts.

$$1\,\ell = 1000\ \text{ml}$$

A medicine spoon holds 5 millilitres.

Complete these.

1 $6\ell = \blacksquare$ ml

2 7000 ml $= \blacksquare\,\ell$

3 $2\frac{1}{2}\,\ell = \blacksquare$ ml

4 $1\frac{1}{4}\,\ell = \blacksquare$ ml

5 $\frac{3}{4}\,\ell = \blacksquare$ ml

6 5250 ml $= \blacksquare\,\ell$

7 Each of these containers of milk holds 500 ml.

How many litres are there altogether?

149

1 How many 250 ml bottles can be filled from the container of milk?

2 How many 400 ml bottles can be filled from the container?

3 How many 500 ml bottles can be filled from two of these containers?

4 How many millilitres are there in one-tenth of a litre?

5 How many 5 ml doses of medicine are there in $\frac{1}{4}$ litre of medicine?

6 Twenty small glasses can be filled from a litre. How many millilitres does each glass hold?

7 How many 600 ml bottles can be filled from 6 litres?

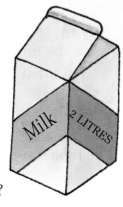

150

1 Kevin had 2300 picture cards. After he had given some of them away, he still had 1700 left. How many had he given away?

2 What number do you get when you divide the product of 16 and 5 by 10?

3 What fraction of these cars is red?

4 Large school photographs cost 90p and small photographs 60p. How much must be paid altogether for 4 large and 4 small photographs?

5 How many $\frac{1}{4}$ litre glasses could be filled from a jug holding $1\frac{1}{2}$ litres of lemonade?

6 A train travelled 39 kilometres in 30 minutes. At the same speed how far would it travel in an hour?

7 How many $\frac{1}{2}$ cm are there in $\frac{1}{2}$ m?

151

The time shown by the first clock can be
written in two ways: **12.20** or **20 past 12.**

The time shown by the second clock is: **1.25** or **25 past 1.**

Now write these times both ways.

1   2   3   4

5   6   7

152

When the minute hand has left half past it is much
easier to work out the number of minutes **to the next
hour**. We say **20 minutes to 3** instead of **40 minutes
past 2**. Write out the times shown on the clocks below.

**10 to 3
or 2.50**

1   2   3

4   5   6   7

153

> On some timetables ten minutes past one in the morning
> is written 1.10 **am** and ten minutes past one in the afternoon
> is written 1.10 **pm**.

> Twenty minutes to nine in the morning is written 8.40 **am** and twenty
> minutes to nine in the evening is written 8.40 **pm**.

Write these times in the same way.
1 Sixteen minutes past five in the morning.
2 Ten minutes past two in the afternoon.
3 Twenty to nine in the morning.
4 A quarter to eight in the evening.
5 Write 7.40 am in words.
6 Write 3.17 pm in words.
7 Write 10.30 am in words.

154

1 How long is it from ten to five until ten past five?
2 A clock shows 5 minutes to 3. The clock is ten
  minutes slow. What is the correct time?
3 The time is now a quarter to one. What will
  be the time in half an hour?
4 A twenty-minute TV programme started at
  ten past two. At what time did it finish?
5 The school clock is a quarter of an hour fast. What is
  the correct time when the school clock shows five past two?
6 What is the time three-quarters of an hour after 2.30?
7 How many minutes are there from twenty-five
  to nine to five past nine?

155

> There are **60 seconds** in **1 minute**.
> There are **60 minutes** in **1 hour**.

second or **s**

minute or **min**

hour or **h**

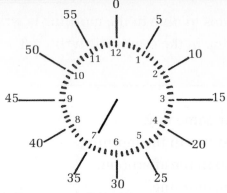

1 How many minutes are there in 10 hours?

2 How many minutes are there in $2\frac{1}{2}$ hours?

3 How many minutes less than an hour is 35 minutes?

4 How many minutes are there in 1 h 40 min?

5 How many seconds are there in 5 minutes?

6 How many seconds are there in 3 min 20 s?

7 How many minutes are there in 360 seconds?

156

1 What day of the week is 8th July?

2 What day of the week is 12th July?

3 What day of the week is 14th July?

4 What is the date of the third Tuesday in July?

5 What day of the week is 30th June?

6 Jane's birthday is 29th July.
   What day of the week is this?

7 How many Mondays are there in this month?

157

1 How many days are there altogether
in April, May and June?

2 How many months of the year have 30 days?

3 How many days are there altogether
in December and January?

4 How many days are there from 21st April to 8th May?

5 How many days are there from 20th November
to 10th December?

6 How many days are there from 5th June to 5th July?

7 How many days are there from Christmas Day
to New Year's Day?

Calendar	January	February	March	April
Sun	6 13 20 27	3 10 17 24	3 10 17 24 31	7 14 21 28
Mon	7 14 21 28	4 11 18 25	4 11 18 25	1 8 15 22 29
Tue	1 8 15 22 29	5 12 19 26	5 12 19 26	2 9 16 23 30
Wed	2 9 16 23 30	6 13 20 27	6 13 20 27	3 10 17 24
Thu	3 10 17 24 31	7 14 21 28	7 14 21 28	4 11 18 25
Fri	4 11 18 25	1 8 15 22	1 8 15 22 29	5 12 19 26
Sat	5 12 19 26	2 9 16 23	2 9 16 23 30	6 13 20 27

	May	June	July	August
Sun	5 12 19 26	2 9 16 23 30	7 14 21 28	4 11 18 25
Mon	6 13 20 27	3 10 17 24	1 8 15 22 29	5 12 19 26
Tue	7 14 21 28	4 11 18 25	2 9 16 23 30	6 13 20 27
Wed	1 8 15 22 29	5 12 19 26	3 10 17 24 31	7 14 21 28
Thu	2 9 16 23 30	6 13 20 27	4 11 18 25	1 8 15 22 29
Fri	3 10 17 24 31	7 14 21 28	5 12 19 26	2 9 16 23 30
Sat	4 11 18 25	1 8 15 22 29	6 13 20 27	3 10 17 24 31

	September	October	November	December
Sun	1 8 15 22 29	6 13 20 27	3 10 17 24	1 8 15 22 29
Mon	2 9 16 23 30	7 14 21 28	4 11 18 25	2 9 16 23 30
Tue	3 10 17 24	1 8 15 22 29	5 12 19 26	3 10 17 24 31
Wed	4 11 18 25	2 9 16 23 30	6 13 20 27	4 11 18 25
Thu	5 12 19 26	3 10 17 24 31	7 14 21 28	5 12 19 26
Fri	6 13 20 27	4 11 18 25	1 8 15 22 29	6 13 20 27
Sat	7 14 21 28	5 12 19 26	2 9 16 23 30	7 14 21 28

158

Use the time line to answer the questions below.

1 Jacob, a seaside donkey, was born in 1969. How old was he in 1984?

2 A boy was 7 years old in 1985. In what year was he born?

3 A dog lived for exactly 13 years. He was born in 1969. In what year did he die?

4 A school was 14 years old in 1981. In what year was it built?

5 Ann started school in 1974 at the age of 5. In what year was she 11 years of age?

6 David was born in 1977. His uncle is 18 years older. In what year was his
uncle born?

7 A young man joined the army in 1984, at the age of 19. In what year was
he born?

159

1. Write 9050 in words.
2. The sum of two numbers is 411. One of the numbers is 101. What is the other number?
3. What fraction of this shape is coloured red?

4. $5 \times 3 \times 3 \times 2 \times 1 = \blacksquare$
5. A cycle horn costs £3·17. How many pence is this?
6. What is the weight in kilograms of 10 parcels each weighing 500 grams?
7. John awoke at 8 am and went to sleep that night at 9.30 pm. How long was he awake?

160

1. Write the numeral which goes in place of ■.
   $$3000 + 4 + 60 + 200 = \blacksquare$$
2. Copy, and write >, < or = in place of ◯.
   $$50 - 14 \ ◯ \ (6 \times 2) + (6 \times 3)$$
3. David saved up for this diver's watch. He saved 50p each week. For how many weeks did he save?
4. A prize of £1000 was divided equally between 3 men and 2 women. How much did each person have?
5. How many 5 cm pieces can be cut from a half-metre strip of cardboard?
6. Half a kilogram of roasted peanuts costs £3. How much would 100 grams cost?
7. When it is full, this jug can hold 1 litre. How many millilitres does it hold now?

161

1. Which of these numerals

   | 4630 | | 3604 | | 3064 | | 6403 |

   can be used to make this a true sentence?
   $$3406 > \blacksquare$$

2. Solve this equation: $15 + 40 = 90 - \boldsymbol{n}$.
3. A quarter of a sum of money is 90p. What is the sum of money in pounds and pence?
4. How much is left from £50 after spending £0·50?
5. Look at the picture on the right. How much more do the ice skates cost than the roller skates?
6. Find a third of 1 m and 20 cm.
7. A box holds a kilogram of tomatoes. If each tomato weighs 50 grams, how many are in the box?

162

1 Write in digits the number that is 1010 less than 10 780.
2 Find a half of five thousand and write the answer in digits.
3 A bag holds £2 in fives. How many coins are there?
4 What is the cost of two concert tickets at £5·55 each?
5 Work out the distance in kilometres from Laneton to Datchlade.

6 What is the total weight in kilograms of 8 packets of butter
each weighing 250 grams?

7 On this digital clock the hours are shown in order from 1 to 12.
Minutes past the hour are shown in order from 1 to 59.
What time was shown one minute later?

163

1 Subtract ten from ten thousand and
write the answer in digits
2 Two boys agreed to share equally all the nuts
they picked. Ali picked 43 and Kevin 17.
How many did each boy have?
3 Solve the equation: $\dfrac{250}{2} - n = 100$.

4 How many 20p coins would be needed to
pay for the pocket radio on the right?
5 Work out the cost of 4 m and 50 cm of wire
costing 8p a metre.
6 A family buys $1\frac{1}{2}$ litres of milk a day. How many
litres would this be during the month of June?
7 $1\frac{1}{2}$ kg + 600 g = ■ kg and ▲ g

°C

164

1 Find the sum of 7070 and seven hundred and seven.

2 Write this subtraction in full:

$$- \; 7 \; 8$$
$$\underline{ \; 2 \; 3}$$

3 Each space on this thermometer on the right
stands for 2 degrees Celsius (2 °C).
The reading on this thermometer is ■°C.

4 A full-grown male giraffe at London Zoo is
$5\frac{3}{4}$ metres in height. How many centimetres is this?

5 A dozen golf-balls cost £6. How much is one ball worth?

6 Find the total of £0·15, £0·67 and £0·85.

7 A parcel weighs 50 grams more than a kilogram.
What is its weight in grams?

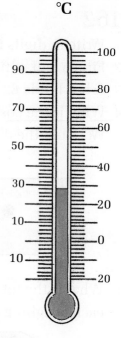

165

1 Add ninety and nineteen.

2 What is the difference between 500 and 50?

3 Find the total of 387, 15 and 85.

4 Subtract 10 from 10 000.

5 Write the missing numerals.

150,   300,   ■,   600,   750,   900,   ■

6 Write this equation in full: $6666 = 6000 + 606 +$ ■.

7 $35 + 78 + 65 =$ ■

166

1 Write this equation in full: $(0 + 17) + (17 - 0) =$ ■.

2 What is $\frac{1}{4}$ of 6000?

3 What number does **n** stand for in this equation?

$$n + 650 + 200 = 1000$$

4 Find a third of nine hundred and fifteen.

5 $\frac{1}{8}$ of a number is 250. What is the number?

6 If I divide a number by 20, the quotient is 50. What is the number?

7 Take 17 times 0 from 17 times 10.

167

1 What is the missing numeral in this equation?

$$93 \times 8 = 8 \times \blacksquare$$

2 Find the product of 2, 9 and 50.

3 Add 6×17 and 4×17.

4 Write this addition equation as a multiplication.

$$54 + 54 + 54 + 54 + 54 = \blacksquare \times \blacktriangle = \blacksquare$$

5 The product of two numbers is 72. One number is 8.
What is the other number?

6 What number when multiplied by 7 is 4 less than 60?

7 What is the remainder when 70 is divided by 9?

168

1 Add one hundred and one to $\boxed{1001}$ and write the answer in words.

2 Subtract the sum of 7 and 7 from the product of 7 and 7.

3 $2550 + 67 + 50 + 3 = \blacksquare$

4 $(15 \times 0) + (15 \times 10) + (15 \times 1) = \blacksquare$

5 $(7 \times 8) - (9 \times 6) = \blacksquare$

6 Three times a certain a number is twenty-seven.
What is one third of that number?

7 What number does **n** stand for in this equation?

$$n \times 40 = 280$$

169

1 How many tens are equal in value to £10·10?

2 How many fives are equal in value to £1·05?

3 How many twos are equal in value to 2 fifties?

4 How many twenties are equal in value to £2·00?

5 How many fifties are equal in value to £50?

6 How many pennies are equal in value to 2 twenties,
2 tens, 2 fives and 2 twos?

7 97p = 3 twenties, $\blacksquare$ fives and 2 pennies.

170

1 Change 80 fives into pounds.
2 Find the cost of 54 chocolate letters at 6 for 5p.
3 How many envelopes at 50 for 30p can you buy for £1·50?
4 How many albums at 90p each can you buy for £6·30?
5 Find the total of £0·70, £16·00, £0·30 and £0·04.
6 £2·20 − £0·45 = £ ▮
7 How much change would you have from £10
   if you spend £1·01?

171

1 What is the cost of 2 slices of melon at 36p a slice?
2 Work out the cost of buying 5 pencil sharpeners
   at 60p each.
3 How much would I pay for 2 frisbees at £2·80 each?
4 Four pears cost 52p. What is the cost of one?
5 Share £3·50 equally among 7 people.
   How much does each person have?
6 What is the cost of 1 ballpoint pen, if 10 cost £9·00?
7 Ten oranges cost £1·70. What is the cost of one?

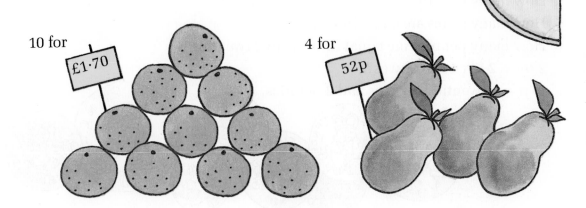

10 for £1·70

4 for 52p

172

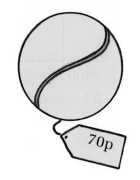

1 Change 100 twenties into pounds.
2 A bag holds £5 in fives. How many coins are in the bag?
3 What is the change from £10, if you spend £2·20?
4 Add £2·20, £0·20, £2·02 and £2·00.
5 62p + 90p + 8p = £ ▮
6 What is the cost of 10 tennis balls at 70p each?
7 I paid £3·50 for ten fruit pies. How much were they each?

173

1 7 m and 42 cm = ▮ cm
2 4 m 70 cm + 90 cm = ▮ m and ▲ cm
3 70 cm − $\frac{1}{2}$ m = ▮ cm
4 $1\frac{1}{4}$ m − 10 cm = ▮ cm
5 60 cm × 6 = ▮ m and ▲ cm
6 1 m 60 cm ÷ 4 = ▮ cm
7 How many 10 cm lengths are there in 10 metres?

174

Find the cost of:
1 50 cm at 30p per metre.
2 17 cm at £1 per metre.
3 200 cm at £2 per metre.
4 6 m 50 cm at 6p per metre.
5 10 m at 19p per metre.
6 20 cm at 20p per metre.
7 75 cm at £4 per metre.

175

| **1 km = 1000 m** |

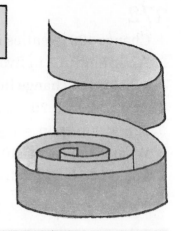

1 2300 m = ■ km and ▲ m

2 8 km and 80 m = ■ m

3 $\frac{1}{2}$ km − 250 m = ■ m

4 900 m + ■ m = 2 km

5 500 m × 8 = ■ km

6 5 km ÷ 2 = ■ m

7 How many 50 m lengths are there in $\frac{1}{2}$ km?

176

1 6006 cm = ■ m and 6 cm

2 9 m − 9 cm = ■ cm

3 Find the cost of 120 cm at 20p per metre.

4 How many 50 cm lengths are there in 5 metres?

5 1 m 60 cm + 1 m 40 cm = ■ m

6 $\frac{1}{4}$ km = 200 m + ■ m

7 2020 m = ■ km and ▲ m

177

1 4 kg = ■ g

2 3 kg and 3 g = ■ g

3 7070 g = ■ kg and ▲ g

4 90 g + ■ g = 1 kg

5 How many half-kilograms are there in 2500 grams?

6 What is the total weight in kilograms of 1000
packets of seeds each weighing 7 grams?

7 How many grams less than 1 kg is 909 g?

178

1 600 g + 300 g + 700 g + 400 g = ⬛ kg
2 Add and change to grams: $\frac{1}{4}$ kg and 800 g.
3 $\frac{3}{4}$ kg − 500 g = ⬛ g
4 400 g × 10 = ⬛ kg
5 2 kg ÷ 10 = ⬛ g
6 Some packets of seeds weigh 9 kg. Each packet weighs 9 g. How many packets are there?
7 What is the total weight in kilograms of a dozen packets of butter each weighing 500 g?

179

Find the cost of:

1 5000 g at 8p per kg.
2 500 g at £1·20 per kg.
3 250 g at 32p per kg.
4 125 g at 64p per kg.
5 100 g at 70p per kg.
6 200 g at 55p per kg.
7 750 g at 12p per kg.

180

1 8 kg 80 g = ⬛ g
2 1 kg − 1 g = ⬛ g
3 What is the cost of 250 g at £4 per $\frac{1}{2}$ kg?
4 300 g × ⬛ = 3 kg
5 1800 g + 9 kg 200 g = ⬛ kg
6 800 g = $\frac{1}{2}$ kg + ⬛ g
7 970 g + ⬛ g = 1 kg 10 g

l litre = 1000 ml

181

1 $3\ell = \blacksquare$ ml

2 $4\frac{1}{2}\ell = \blacksquare$ ml

3 7 l and 70 ml = $\blacksquare$ ml

4 5ℓ and 5 ml = $\blacksquare$ ml

5 1010 ml = $\blacksquare\ell$ ▲ ml

6 $1\ell - 100$ ml = $\blacksquare$ ml

7 900 ml x 10 = $\blacksquare\ell$

182

1 How many millilitres are there in $\frac{1}{5}$ litre?

2 How many millilitres must be added to 800 ml to make a litre?

3 How many millilitres more than $\frac{1}{2}\ell$ is 550 ml?

4 How many 250 ml tins of paint are needed to make 1 ℓ?

5 How many 500 ml tins are needed to make 5 ℓ?

6 How many 25 ml measures can be filled from $\frac{1}{4}\ell$?

7 How many 50 ml measures can be filled from $\frac{1}{2}\ell$?

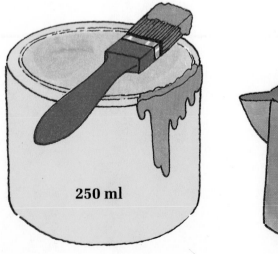

250 ml

25 ml